CGP

Mental Maths

Key Stage 2
For ages 9-11

Practise & Learn

Published by CGP

Editors:
David Broadbent
Chris Lindle
Rebecca Tate

Updated by Ruth Wilbourne

With thanks to Rob Harrison for the proofreading.

ISBN: 978 1 84762 964 7

Printed by Elanders Ltd, Newcastle upon Tyne
Clipart from Corel®

Contents

Addition

Doing additions in your head can be tricky. One way to make it easier is to split up one of the numbers. Here's an example:

14300 + 2500 = ?

Split up the smaller number. For example, 2500 splits into **thousands** and **hundreds**.

2000 and 500

Add the **thousands** to the bigger number...

14300 + 2000 = 16300

... then add the **hundreds** to get the answer.

16300 + 500 = 16800

Split the smaller number and fill in the boxes to work out the answer.

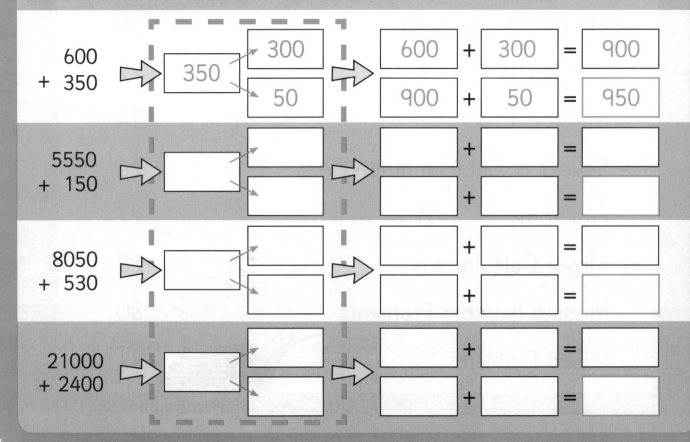

600 + 350 → 350 → 300, 50 → 600 + 300 = 900, 900 + 50 = 950

5550 + 150

8050 + 530

21000 + 2400

Use mental maths to answer the questions below.

Add 2900 to 13000. `15900`

What is 5342 plus 550?

What is the sum of 3600 and 14120?

What is 12200 add 7300?

What is the total of 7200 and 10420?

Add 5100 and 16410.

What is the sum of 23500 and 9200?

Write the answers to the questions below.
See how fast you can do them all.

500 + 460 =	`960`	11400 + 8100 =	
600 + 350 =		6400 + 13200 =	
220 + 300 =		4200 + 10259 =	
380 + 510 =		15703 + 2100 =	
180 + 900 =		8400 + 11202 =	
650 + 520 =		13296 + 4100 =	
3020 + 710 =		5100 + 16100 =	
380 + 6400 =		23134 + 2300 =	
660 + 2300 =		15634 + 3400 =	

Subtraction

Doing subtractions in your head can be tricky. One way to make it easier is to split up one of the numbers.

Here's an example: ➡ **16600 – 2400 = ?**

Split up the smaller number. For example, 2400 splits into **thousands** and **hundreds**.

2000 and **400**

Subtract the **thousands** from the bigger number...

16600 – 2000 = 14600

... then subtract the **hundreds** to get the answer.

14600 – 400 = 14200

Split the smaller number and fill in the boxes to work out the answer.

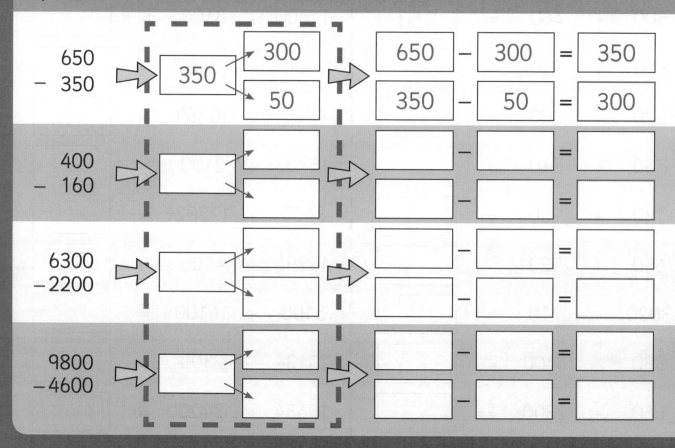

| 650 – 350 | ➡ | 350 | → 300 → 50 | ➡ | 650 | – | 300 | = | 350 |
| | | | | | 350 | – | 50 | = | 300 |

| 400 – 160 | ➡ | | | ➡ | | – | | = | |
| | | | | | | – | | = | |

| 6300 – 2200 | ➡ | | | ➡ | | – | | = | |
| | | | | | | – | | = | |

| 9800 – 4600 | ➡ | | | ➡ | | – | | = | |
| | | | | | | – | | = | |

Use mental maths to answer the questions below.

Subtract 260 from 590.	330
What is 700 minus 480?	
What is the difference between 3600 and 2400?	
What is 19200 take away 7100?	
Subtract 6600 from 18800.	
What is 17500 minus 3400?	
What is the difference between 10550 and 2300?	

Write the answers to the questions below.
See how fast you can do them all.

680 – 420 =	260	12450 – 2400 =
720 – 320 =		16930 – 3400 =
800 – 350 =		14870 – 2800 =
900 – 620 =		15740 – 5200 =
2400 – 1400 =		17850 – 2600 =
3600 – 2400 =		13296 – 1100 =
8700 – 4300 =		25645 – 4300 =
19700 – 5200 =		23237 – 5100 =
14200 – 3100 =		24654 – 7200 =

Decimals

When you add a whole number to a decimal, just add the whole numbers and leave the tenths as they are. ⟹ $12 + 2.3 = 14.3$

When you subtract a decimal from a whole number, you can count on from the smaller number to the bigger number. Here's an example: ⟹ $10 - 7.6 = ?$

Count on in **tenths** to the nearest whole number. $7.6 + 0.4 = 8$

Then count on in **ones** to the bigger number. $8 + 2 = 10$

Add together the numbers you've counted on by to get the answer. $2 + 0.4 = 2.4$

Write the answers to these questions in the boxes.

7 + 2.5 =	9.5		8 − 6.5 =	1.5
5 + 1.8 =			10 − 4.3 =	
9 + 4.4 =			7 − 0.4 =	
14 + 3.6 =			14 − 10.1 =	
11 + 7.7 =			18 − 17.3 =	
7 + 2.25 =			15 − 6.9 =	
10 + 17.11 =			26 − 12.8 =	
13 + 12.45 =			28 − 17.1 =	
15 + 13.85 =			23 − 6.5 =	

When you add or subtract two decimal numbers,
you can split them up to make it easier.
Here's an example of subtracting decimals: **4.2 – 2.1 = ?**

Split up the smaller decimal. **2.1** ⇨ **2** and **0.1**

Subtract the **units** from the bigger decimal... **4.2 – 2 = 2.2**

... then subtract the **tenths** to get the answer. **2.2 – 0.1 = 2.1**

Draw a line between each calculation and its correct answer.

8.5 + 1.4

8.9

11.5

5.9 – 3.4

9.9

3.3 + 1.6

4.9 – 3.7

9.0

2.5

1.2

7.2 + 4.3

10.7 – 1.8

4.9

4.1

6.4 + 2.6

12.5 – 8.4

Read the questions below. Write your answers in the boxes.

Janet buys 1.7 kg of potatoes and 2.6 kg of carrots.
What is the total weight of her shopping?
☐ kg

Sarah has 3.7 l of fizzy drink. She spills 1.4 l.
How many litres of fizzy drink does she have left?
☐ l

In a long jump competition, Maya jumps 3.3 m and Penny jumps
2.7 m. What is the difference between the lengths of their jumps?
☐ m

Jane drives 13.4 km to get to the shops. She then drives
another 8.4 km to get to the beach. How far has she driven?
☐ km

9

Negative Numbers

Negative numbers are numbers that are less than 0. When you do additions or subtractions with negative numbers, count on or back to work out the answer. Here's an example: ➡ **-3 – 4 = ?**

Count back **4** from **-3**. ➡
| –1 | –1 | –1 | –1 |
-7   -6   -5   -4   -3
➡ so **-3 – 4 = -7**

Draw a line to match each calculation with the correct answer.

-13 + 8

-3 – 2

-9 + 3

-6 – 8

-5

-4

-5

-1

-10

-6

-20

-14

-4 – 6

-8 + 4

-12 – 8

-2 + 1

Use mental maths to answer the questions below.

It is -1 °C in Cardiff. In Brussels it is 5 °C colder. What is the temperature in Brussels? `-6` °C

In Toronto it is 4 °C colder than it is in New York. It is -6 °C in New York. What is the temperature in Toronto? `☐` °C

It is -5 °C in Manchester. It is 3 °C warmer in Bristol. What is the temperature in Bristol? `☐` °C

In Berlin it is 2 °C warmer than it is in Paris. It is -8 °C in Paris. What is the temperature in Berlin? `☐` °C

Some calculations go through 0. These are easier if you count on or back to 0 first. Here's an example:

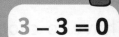

3 – 7 = ?

Count back from **3** until you get to **0**.   **3 – 3 = 0**

Work out how much of the big number is left.   **7 – 3 = 4**

Subtract this from **0** to find the answer.   **0 – 4 = -4**

Fill in the boxes to find the answer to each question.

| 5 – 7 | ⇒ | 5 [– 5] 0 [– 2] -2 |
| -7 + 9 | ⇒ | -7 [ ] 0 [ ] [ ] |

| -4 + 5 | ⇒ | -4 [ ] 0 [ ] [ ] |
| 2 – 8 | ⇒ | 2 [ ] 0 [ ] [ ] |

| 3 – 9 | ⇒ | 3 [ ] 0 [ ] [ ] |
| -6 + 14 | ⇒ | -6 [ ] 0 [ ] [ ] |

Work out the questions below and write the answers in the boxes.

-4   +   6   =   [2]   -5   +   9   =   [ ]

3   –   7   =   [ ]   2   –   8   =   [ ]

-2   +   8   =   [ ]   -7   +   13   =   [ ]

4   –   12   =   [ ]   11   –   16   =   [ ]

Problem Solving

Some questions don't tell you which calculations to use.
You have to choose a good way to work out the answer.
Here's an example:

Bruno is having a new bath fitted for **£300** and his roof fixed for **£1300**. He starts with **£1800**. How much will he have left over?

Add up the amount Bruno spends:
£300 + **£1300** = **£1600**

Then subtract this from the amount he starts with:
£1800 – **£1600** = **£200**

Work out the problems below in your head.

A theatre has 2500 seats. If 1500 seats are booked for a play, how many are left over?

Kelsey has a desk that is 1.3 m long and a table that is 1.2 m long. She puts them next to each other. How long are they altogether?

4500 people visit a country fair on the first day. 600 fewer people visit on the second day. How many people visit on the second day?

Pasha buys a jumper and a kettle for a total of £40.00. The jumper costs £25.50. How much does the kettle cost?

£

360 passengers are on a cruise ship. At the next port, 150 passengers get off and 220 passengers get on. How many passengers are on the ship now?

A skyscraper has floors above ground numbered from 0 up to 20 and floors underground numbered from -1 down to -10.
Use this information to answer these questions in the boxes.

If you take the lift from floor 15 down to floor -3, how many floors will you travel?

If you travel up 10 floors from floor -4, which floor will you end up on?

If you start on floor 5, travel down 14 floors, then back up 6 floors, which floor will you end up on?

Work out the problems below in your head.

Patrick's car is 4600 mm long and his garage is 5950 mm long. How much longer is his garage than his car?

mm

Shauna needs 3.5 l of milk. She buys 2.4 l from the shop. How much more milk does she need?

l

A town has 3600 people living in it.
23000 people live in another town nearby.
How many people live in the two towns in total?

Tina buys a bag of apples costing £2.50 and a cauliflower costing £1.30. She pays with a £10 note.
How much change should she get?

£

Jamal's bag weighs 5 kg. Josh has two bags —
one weighs 1.5 kg more than Jamal's bag
and the other weighs 2 kg less than Jamal's bag.
What is the total weight of Josh's bags?

kg

13

Multiplying by 10, 100 & 1000

To multiply by 10, 100 or 1000, move the digits to the left along the place value columns. For example:

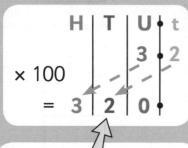

Move one space to multiply by 10.

T	U
	7

× 10

= 7 | 0

Move two spaces to multiply by 100.

Move three spaces to multiply by 1000.

H	T	U	t
		0	6

× 1000

= 6 | 0 | 0

Fill in the boxes to complete the calculations.

63	×	100	=	6300		35	×	1000	=	
9	×	1000	=			1.72	×	10	=	
53	×	10	=			0.3	×	10	=	
29	×	100	=			0.4	×	1000	=	
66	×	1000	=			12.6	×	100	=	

Use multiplication to solve the problems below.

If a ship travels 236.4 km each day, how far does it travel in 10 days? _____ km

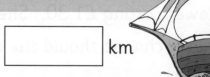

A shop sells 1000 dresses for £25.50 each. What is the total price of the dresses sold? £ _____

Jerry can move 100 crates every hour. If he works for 7.5 hours, how many crates can he move? _____

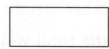

Dividing by 10, 100 & 1000

To divide by 10, 100 or 1000, move the digits to the right along the place value columns. For example:

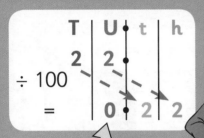

$\div 100 =$

Move two spaces to divide by 100.

Move one space to divide by 10.

$\div 10 =$

Move three spaces to divide by 1000.

$\div 1000 =$

Fill in the boxes to complete the calculations.

7.3 ÷ 10 =	**0.73**	112 ÷ 100 =
6 ÷ 100 =		84.5 ÷ 10 =
242 ÷ 10 =		0.4 ÷ 10 =
9300 ÷ 1000 =		47 ÷ 1000 =
137 ÷ 1000 =		741 ÷ 100 =

Divide each number by 10, 100 and 1000.

	÷ 10	÷ 100	÷ 1000		÷ 10	÷ 100	÷ 1000
26	2.6	0.26	0.026	1238			
460				124			
7160				9198			

Multiplication Facts

You can use multiplication facts to help you do tricky calculations. Here's an example: ➡ **70 × 80 = ?**

Using your times tables you know that   **7 × 8 = 56**

70 and **80** are 10 times bigger than **7** and **8**. The answer must be **100** times bigger than **56**.

56 × 100 = 5600

Fill in the boxes to complete the calculations.

70	×	4	=	280	120	×	90	=
60	×	40	=		40	×	5	=
30	×	2	=		20	×	800	=
80	×	80	=		30	×	110	=
50	×	6	=		1200	×	40	=

Fill in the boxes to make the correct calculations.

8	×	20	=	160	70	×		= 2100
	×	3	=	120		×	60	= 420
30	×		=	1500	400	×		= 36000
	×	20	=	1800		×	40	= 32000

16

Practise and Learn

Mental Maths

Ages 9-11

Answers

This section shows each of the pages from the book with the answers filled in.

The pages are laid out in the same way as the book itself, so the questions can be easily marked by you, or by your child.

There are also helpful learning tips with some of the pages.

4

Addition

Doing additions in your head can be tricky. One way to make it easier is to split up one of the numbers. Here's an example: ➡ **14300 + 2500 = ?**

Split up the smaller number. For example, 2500 splits into **thousands** and **hundreds**. → **2000 and 500**

Add the **thousands** to the bigger number... → **14300 + 2000 = 16300**

... then add the **hundreds** to get the answer. → **16300 + 500 = 16800**

Split the smaller number and fill in the boxes to work out the answer.

600 + 350	⇨ 350	300	600 + 300 = 900
		50	900 + 50 = 950
5550 + 150	⇨ 150	100	5550 + 100 = 5650
		50	5650 + 50 = 5700
8050 + 530	⇨ 530	500	8050 + 500 = 8550
		30	8550 + 30 = 8580
21000 + 2400	⇨ 2400	2000	21000 + 2000 = 23000
		400	23000 + 400 = 23400

4

5

Use mental maths to answer the questions below.

Add 2900 to 13000.	15900
What is 5342 plus 550?	**5892**
What is the sum of 3600 and 14120?	**17720**
What is 12200 add 7300?	**19500**
What is the total of 7200 and 10420?	**17620**
Add 5100 and 16410.	**21510**
What is the sum of 23500 and 9200?	**32700**

Write the answers to the questions below.
See how fast you can do them all.

500	+	460	=	960	11400	+	8100	=	**19500**
600	+	350	=	**950**	6400	+	13200	=	**19600**
220	+	300	=	**520**	4200	+	10259	=	**14459**
380	+	510	=	**890**	15703	+	2100	=	**17803**
180	+	900	=	**1080**	8400	+	11202	=	**19602**
650	+	520	=	**1170**	13296	+	4100	=	**17396**
3020	+	710	=	**3730**	5100	+	16100	=	**21200**
380	+	6400	=	**6780**	23134	+	2300	=	**25434**
660	+	2300	=	**2960**	15634	+	3400	=	**19034**

5

Encourage your child to use the splitting technique for tricky additions.

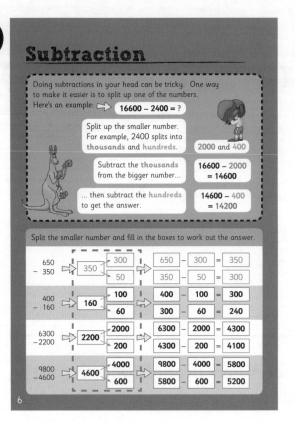

6 Subtraction

Doing subtractions in your head can be tricky. One way to make it easier is to split up one of the numbers.
Here's an example: ➡ **16600 – 2400 = ?**

Split up the smaller number. For example, 2400 splits into **thousands** and **hundreds**. → **2000 and 400**

Subtract the **thousands** from the bigger number... → **16600 – 2000 = 14600**

... then subtract the **hundreds** to get the answer. → **14600 – 400 = 14200**

Split the smaller number and fill in the boxes to work out the answer.

650 – 350	→ 350	300 / 50	650 – 300 = 350	350 – 50 = 300
400 – 160	→ 160	100 / 60	400 – 100 = 300	300 – 60 = 240
6300 – 2200	→ 2200	2000 / 200	6300 – 2000 = 4300	4300 – 200 = 4100
9800 – 4600	→ 4600	4000 / 600	9800 – 4000 = 5800	5800 – 600 = 5200

6

7

Use mental maths to answer the questions below.

Subtract 260 from 590.	330
What is 700 minus 480?	220
What is the difference between 3600 and 2400?	1200
What is 19200 take away 7100?	12100
Subtract 6600 from 18800.	12200
What is 17500 minus 3400?	14100
What is the difference between 10550 and 2300?	8250

Write the answers to the questions below.
See how fast you can do them all.

680	–	420	= 260	12450	– 2400	= 10050
720	–	320	= 400	16930	– 3400	= 13530
800	–	350	= 450	14870	– 2800	= 12070
900	–	620	= 280	15740	– 5200	= 10540
2400	–	1400	= 1000	17850	– 2600	= 15250
3600	–	2400	= 1200	13296	– 1100	= 12196
8700	–	4300	= 4400	25645	– 4300	= 21345
19700	–	5200	= 14500	23237	– 5100	= 18137
14200	–	3100	= 11100	24654	– 7200	= 17454

7

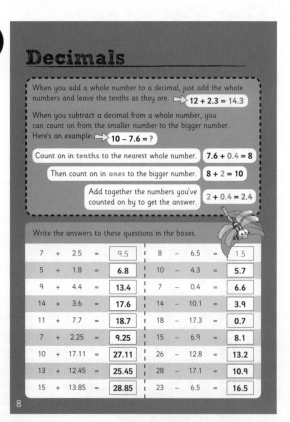

8 Decimals

When you add a whole number to a decimal, just add the whole numbers and leave the tenths as they are. ➡ **12 + 2.3 = 14.3**

When you subtract a decimal from a whole number, you can count on from the smaller number to the bigger number.
Here's an example: ➡ **10 – 7.6 = ?**

Count on in **tenths** to the nearest whole number. → **7.6 + 0.4 = 8**

Then count on in **ones** to the bigger number. → **8 + 2 = 10**

Add together the numbers you've counted on by to get the answer. → **2 + 0.4 = 2.4**

Write the answers to these questions in the boxes.

7	+	2.5	=	9.5		8	–	6.5	=	1.5
5	+	1.8	=	6.8		10	–	4.3	=	5.7
9	+	4.4	=	13.4		7	–	0.4	=	6.6
14	+	3.6	=	17.6		14	–	10.1	=	3.9
11	+	7.7	=	18.7		18	–	17.3	=	0.7
7	+	2.25	=	9.25		15	–	6.9	=	8.1
10	+	17.11	=	27.11		26	–	12.8	=	13.2
13	+	12.45	=	25.45		28	–	17.1	=	10.9
15	+	13.85	=	28.85		23	–	6.5	=	16.5

8

9

When you add or subtract two decimal numbers, you can split them up to make it easier.
Here's an example of subtracting decimals: ➡ **4.2 – 2.1 = ?**

Split up the smaller decimal. → **2.1 ➡ 2 and 0.1**

Subtract the **units** from the bigger decimal... → **4.2 – 2 = 2.2**

... then subtract the **tenths** to get the answer. → **2.2 – 0.1 = 2.1**

Draw a line between each calculation and its correct answer.

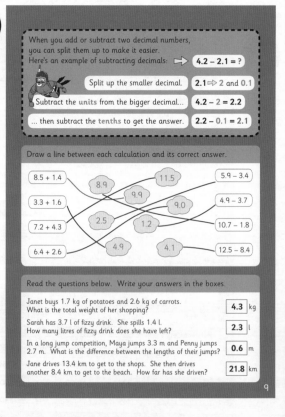

8.5 + 1.4		11.5	5.9 – 3.4
	8.9	9.9	
3.3 + 1.6		9.0	4.9 – 3.7
7.2 + 4.3	2.5	1.2	10.7 – 1.8
6.4 + 2.6	4.9	4.1	12.5 – 8.4

Read the questions below. Write your answers in the boxes.

Janet buys 1.7 kg of potatoes and 2.6 kg of carrots. What is the total weight of her shopping? — **4.3** kg

Sarah has 3.7 l of fizzy drink. She spills 1.4 l. How many litres of fizzy drink does she have left? — **2.3** l

In a long jump competition, Maya jumps 3.3 m and Penny jumps 2.7 m. What is the difference between the lengths of their jumps? — **0.6** m

Jane drives 13.4 km to get to the shops. She then drives another 8.4 km to get to the beach. How far has she driven? — **21.8** km

9

If your child finds decimal questions tricky, help them to identify the tenths and hundredths in each number.

Negative Numbers

Negative numbers are numbers that are less than 0. When you do additions or subtractions with negative numbers, count on or back to work out the answer. Here's an example: ➡ -3 – 4 = ?

Count back 4 from -3.

$$-1 \quad -1 \quad -1 \quad -1$$
$$-7 \quad -6 \quad -5 \quad -4 \quad -3$$

➡ so -3 – 4 = -7

Draw a line to match each calculation with the correct answer.

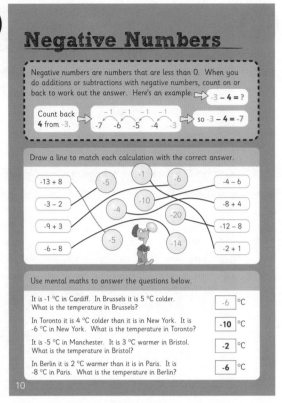

-13 + 8 → -5 → -1 → -6 → -4 – 6

-3 – 2 → -10 → -8 + 4

-9 + 3 → -4 → -20 → -12 – 8

-6 – 8 → -5 → -14 → -2 + 1

Use mental maths to answer the questions below.

It is -1 °C in Cardiff. In Brussels it is 5 °C colder.
What is the temperature in Brussels? **-6** °C

In Toronto it is 4 °C colder than it is in New York. It is
-6 °C in New York. What is the temperature in Toronto? **-10** °C

It is -5 °C in Manchester. It is 3 °C warmer in Bristol.
What is the temperature in Bristol? **-2** °C

In Berlin it is 2 °C warmer than it is in Paris. It is
-8 °C in Paris. What is the temperature in Berlin? **-6** °C

10

A number line might help your child
understand negative numbers at first, but
it's important that they learn to do these
calculations in their head.

Some calculations go through 0. These are easier if you count on or back to 0 first. Here's an example: 3 – 7 = ?

Count back from 3 until you get to **0**. 3 – 3 = 0

Work out how much of the big number is left. 7 – 3 = 4

Subtract this from **0** to find the answer. 0 – 4 = -4

Fill in the boxes to find the answer to each question.

| – 5 | – 2 | | + 7 | + 2 |
5 – 7 ➡ 5 ⌒ 0 ⌒ -2 | -7 + 9 ➡ -7 ⌒ 0 ⌒ 2

| + 4 | + 1 | | – 2 | – 6 |
-4 + 5 ➡ -4 ⌒ 0 ⌒ 1 | 2 – 8 ➡ 2 ⌒ 0 ⌒ -6

| – 3 | – 6 | | + 6 | + 8 |
3 – 9 ➡ 3 ⌒ 0 ⌒ -6 | -6 + 14 ➡ -6 ⌒ 0 ⌒ 8

Work out the questions below and write the answers in the boxes.

-4	+	6	=	2		-5	+	9	=	4
3	–	7	=	-4		2	–	8	=	-6
-2	+	8	=	6		-7	+	13	=	6
4	–	12	=	-8		11	–	16	=	-5

11

Problem Solving

Some questions don't tell you which calculations to use.
You have to choose a good way to work out the answer.
Here's an example:

Bruno is having a new bath fitted for £300 and his roof fixed for £1300. He starts with £1800. How much will he have left over?

➡ Add up the amount Bruno spends:
£300 + £1300 = £1600

Then subtract this from the amount he starts with:
£1800 – £1600 = £200

Work out the problems below in your head.

A theatre has 2500 seats. If 1500 seats are booked for a play, how many are left over? **1000**

Kelsey has a desk that is 1.3 m long and a table that is 1.2 m long. She puts them next to each other. How long are they altogether? **2.5** m

4500 people visit a country fair on the first day. 600 fewer people visit on the second day. How many people visit on the second day? **3900**

Pasha buys a jumper and a kettle for a total of £40.00. The jumper costs £25.50. How much does the kettle cost? £ **14.50**

360 passengers are on a cruise ship. At the next port, 150 passengers get off and 220 passengers get on. How many passengers are on the ship now? **430**

12

If your child struggles with word problems,
get them to write down the calculations
they need to do before they work them out
in their head.

A skyscraper has 20 floors above ground numbered from 0 up to 20 and 10 floors underground numbered from -1 down to -10. Use this information to answer these questions in the boxes.

If you take the lift from floor 15 down to floor -3, how many floors will you travel? **18**

If you travel up 10 floors from floor -4, which floor will you end up on? **6**

If you start on floor 5, travel down 14 floors, then back up 6 floors, which floor will you end up on? **-3**

Work out the problems below in your head.

Patrick's car is 4600 mm long and his garage is 5950 mm long. How much longer is his garage than his car? **1350** mm

Shauna needs 3.5 l of milk. She buys 2.4 l from the shop. How much more milk does she need? **1.1** l

A town has 3600 people living in it. 23000 people live in another town nearby. How many people live in the two towns in total? **26600**

Tina buys a bag of apples costing £2.50 and a cauliflower costing £1.30. She pays with a £10 note. How much change should she get? £ **6.20**

Jamal's bag weighs 5 kg. Josh has two bags — one weighs 1.5 kg more than Jamal's bag and the other weighs 2 kg less than Jamal's bag. What is the total weight of Josh's bags? **9.5** kg

13

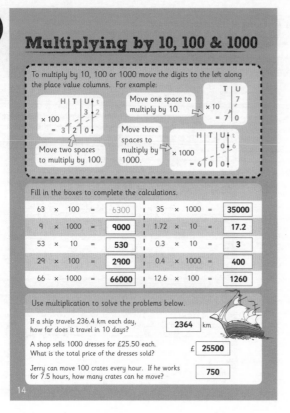

14 — Multiplying by 10, 100 & 1000

To multiply by 10, 100 or 1000 move the digits to the left along the place value columns. For example:

Move one space to multiply by 10.
Move two spaces to multiply by 100.
Move three spaces to multiply by 1000.

Fill in the boxes to complete the calculations.

63 × 100 =	6300		35 × 1000 =	35000
9 × 1000 =	9000		1.72 × 10 =	17.2
53 × 10 =	530		0.3 × 10 =	3
29 × 100 =	2900		0.4 × 1000 =	400
66 × 1000 =	66000		12.6 × 100 =	1260

Use multiplication to solve the problems below.

If a ship travels 236.4 km each day, how far does it travel in 10 days?   **2364** km

A shop sells 1000 dresses for £25.50 each. What is the total price of the dresses sold?   £ **25500**

Jerry can move 100 crates every hour. If he works for 7.5 hours, how many crates can he move?   **750**

14

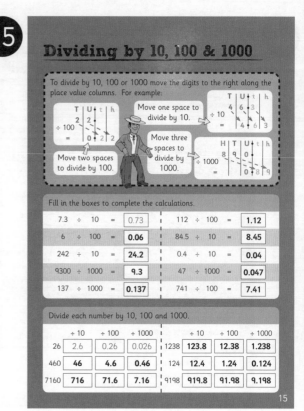

15 — Dividing by 10, 100 & 1000

To divide by 10, 100 or 1000 move the digits to the right along the place value columns. For example:

Move one space to divide by 10.
Move two spaces to divide by 100.
Move three spaces to divide by 1000.

Fill in the boxes to complete the calculations.

7.3 ÷ 10 =	0.73		112 ÷ 100 =	1.12
6 ÷ 100 =	0.06		84.5 ÷ 10 =	8.45
242 ÷ 10 =	24.2		0.4 ÷ 10 =	0.04
9300 ÷ 1000 =	9.3		47 ÷ 1000 =	0.047
137 ÷ 1000 =	0.137		741 ÷ 100 =	7.41

Divide each number by 10, 100 and 1000.

	÷ 10	÷ 100	÷ 1000		÷ 10	÷ 100	÷ 1000
26	2.6	0.26	0.026	1238	123.8	12.38	1.238
460	46	4.6	0.46	124	12.4	1.24	0.124
7160	716	71.6	7.16	9198	919.8	91.98	9.198

15

If your child struggles with multiplying or dividing by 10, 100 & 1000, help them identify how the digits need to move.

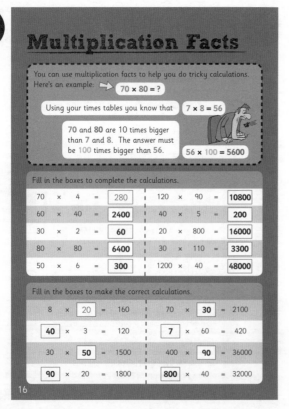

16 — Multiplication Facts

You can use multiplication facts to help you do tricky calculations. Here's an example: 70 × 80 = ?

Using your times tables you know that   7 × 8 = 56

70 and 80 are 10 times bigger than 7 and 8. The answer must be 100 times bigger than 56.   56 × 100 = 5600

Fill in the boxes to complete the calculations.

70 × 4 =	280		120 × 90 =	10800
60 × 40 =	2400		40 × 5 =	200
30 × 2 =	60		20 × 800 =	16000
80 × 80 =	6400		30 × 110 =	3300
50 × 6 =	300		1200 × 40 =	48000

Fill in the boxes to make the correct calculations.

8 × **20** = 160		70 × **30** = 2100
40 × 3 = 120		**7** × 60 = 420
30 × **50** = 1500		400 × **90** = 36000
90 × 20 = 1800		**800** × 40 = 32000

16

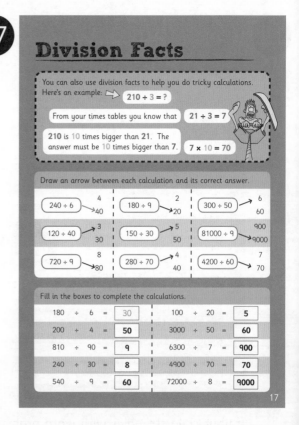

17 — Division Facts

You can also use division facts to help you do tricky calculations. Here's an example: 210 ÷ 3 = ?

From your times tables you know that   21 ÷ 3 = 7

210 is 10 times bigger than 21. The answer must be 10 times bigger than 7.   7 × 10 = 70

Draw an arrow between each calculation and its correct answer.

240 ÷ 6 → 40   (4)
180 ÷ 9 → 20   (2)
300 ÷ 50 → 6   (60)
120 ÷ 40 → 3   (30)
150 ÷ 30 → 5   (50)
81000 ÷ 9 → 9000   (900)
720 ÷ 9 → 80   (8)
280 ÷ 70 → 4   (40)
4200 ÷ 60 → 70   (7)

Fill in the boxes to complete the calculations.

180 ÷ 6 =	30		100 ÷ 20 =	5
200 ÷ 4 =	50		3000 ÷ 50 =	60
810 ÷ 90 =	9		6300 ÷ 7 =	900
240 ÷ 30 =	8		4900 ÷ 70 =	70
540 ÷ 9 =	60		72000 ÷ 8 =	9000

17

Multiplication

You can do some multiplications just by knowing your times tables. For harder multiplications you can split up one of the numbers. Here's an example: ➡ **15 × 7 = ?**

Split the big number into **tens** and **units**.	**15** ➡ **10 and 5**
Multiply the small number by the **tens**...	**7 × 10 = 70**
... then multiply it by the **units**.	**7 × 5 = 35**
Then add them together to get the answer.	**70 + 35 = 105**

Underline the calculation that equals the number in the circle.

(150)	➡	25 × 6	14 × 10	29 × 5	45 × 4
(72)	➡	3 × 40	13 × 4	12 × 6	14 × 8
(39)	➡	16 × 2	15 × 3	19 × 5	13 × 3
(119)	➡	20 × 6	14 × 8	17 × 7	16 × 9

Answer the questions below using multiplication.

Sam has 9 packets that each have 15 cabbage seeds inside. How many seeds does she have altogether?	**135**
Eleanor has 6 pieces of ribbon that are each 21 cm long. What is the total length of the ribbon pieces?	**126** cm
A tin contains 19 biscuits. Solomon buys 8 tins. How many biscuits has he bought?	**152**

Write the answers to the questions below. See how fast you can do them all.

40	×	7	=	280	46	×	3	=	138
50	×	9	=	450	26	×	8	=	208
20	×	3	=	60	42	×	6	=	252
13	×	2	=	26	78	×	4	=	312
15	×	3	=	45	39	×	9	=	351
19	×	2	=	38	84	×	5	=	420
22	×	4	=	88	67	×	6	=	402
15	×	5	=	75	302	×	2	=	604
14	×	3	=	42	230	×	3	=	690
23	×	5	=	115	120	×	5	=	600
30	×	8	=	240	205	×	4	=	820
25	×	7	=	175	160	×	4	=	640
45	×	4	=	180	142	×	2	=	284
65	×	6	=	390	312	×	3	=	936
13	×	6	=	78	3004	×	2	=	6008
19	×	7	=	133	4400	×	2	=	8800
16	×	9	=	144	1020	×	3	=	3060
32	×	8	=	256	2050	×	4	=	8200

To do multiplications like this, it's really important that your child has a solid grasp of their times tables up to 12 x 12. If not, help them practise them regularly.

Multiplication Tricks

You can make multiplying decimal numbers easier by turning them into whole numbers. Here's an example: ➡ **0.6 × 4 = ?**

Multiply the decimal number by **10** to turn it into a whole number.	**0.6 × 10 = 6**
Do the multiplication using the whole number.	**6 × 4 = 24**
The answer is **10** times too big. Divide it by **10** to find the answer.	**24 ÷ 10 = 2.4**

Fill in the boxes to complete the calculations.

0.4	×	4	=	1.6	0.5	×	3	=	1.5
0.6	×	5	=	3.0	0.9	×	8	=	7.2
0.3	×	9	=	2.7	0.8	×	6	=	4.8
0.2	×	8	=	1.6	0.7	×	7	=	4.9

Answer the questions below using multiplication.

A bar of chocolate costs £0.80. How much do 8 bars of chocolate cost?	£ **6.40**
Eleanor needs 0.4 kg of flour to make 1 loaf of bread. How much flour does she need to make 6 loaves?	**2.4** kg
12 people are having lunch. They each drink 0.6 l of juice. How much juice do they drink altogether?	**7.2** l
Jo carries 9 tins that each weigh 0.4 kg. Sam carries 11 tins that each weigh 0.3 kg. Who carries the heaviest load?	**Jo**

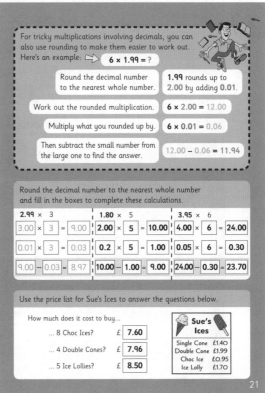

For tricky multiplications involving decimals, you can also use rounding to make them easier to work out. Here's an example: ➡ **6 × 1.99 = ?**

Round the decimal number to the nearest whole number.	**1.99** rounds up to **2.00** by adding **0.01**.
Work out the rounded multiplication.	**6 × 2.00 = 12.00**
Multiply what you rounded up by.	**6 × 0.01 = 0.06**
Then subtract the small number from the large one to find the answer.	**12.00 − 0.06 = 11.94**

Round the decimal number to the nearest whole number and fill in the boxes to complete these calculations.

2.99 × 3		1.80 × 5		3.95 × 6	
3.00 × 3 = 9.00	2.00 × 5 = 10.00	4.00 × 6 = 24.00			
0.01 × 3 = 0.03	0.2 × 5 = 1.00	0.05 × 6 = 0.30			
9.00 − 0.03 = 8.97	10.00 − 1.00 = 9.00	24.00 − 0.30 = 23.70			

Use the price list for Sue's Ices to answer the questions below.

How much does it cost to buy...

... 8 Choc Ices?	£	**7.60**
... 4 Double Cones?	£	**7.96**
... 5 Ice Lollies?	£	**8.50**

Sue's Ices

Single Cone	£1.40
Double Cone	£1.99
Choc Ice	£0.95
Ice Lolly	£1.70

For some more practice, get your child to multiply the prices of a few items on your next shopping trip.

Division

You can do some divisions just by knowing your times tables:

$42 \div 7 = ?$ ➡ From your times tables you know that $7 \times 6 = 42$ so the answer is 6.

With some divisions you might be left with a remainder.
Here's an example: ➡ $75 \div 8 = ?$

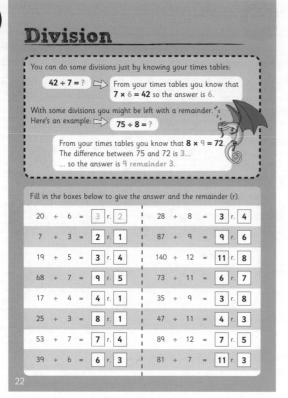

From your times tables you know that $8 \times 9 = 72$.
The difference between 75 and 72 is 3...
... so the answer is 9 remainder 3.

Fill in the boxes below to give the answer and the remainder (r).

20	÷	6	=	**3** r. **2**	28	÷	8	=	**3** r. **4**
7	÷	3	=	**2** r. **1**	87	÷	9	=	**9** r. **6**
19	÷	5	=	**3** r. **4**	140	÷	12	=	**11** r. **8**
68	÷	7	=	**9** r. **5**	73	÷	11	=	**6** r. **7**
17	÷	4	=	**4** r. **1**	35	÷	9	=	**3** r. **8**
25	÷	3	=	**8** r. **1**	47	÷	11	=	**4** r. **3**
53	÷	7	=	**7** r. **4**	89	÷	12	=	**7** r. **5**
39	÷	6	=	**6** r. **3**	81	÷	7	=	**11** r. **3**

Your child will find division much easier if they have a good knowledge of the times tables (up to 12 x 12).

Answer the questions below using division.

Ed packs 38 eggs into boxes of 6. He eats the leftover eggs for his tea. How many eggs does he eat? **2**

There are 58 people at a party. Each table seats 9 people. How many tables are filled up? **6**

76 children want to play in a football tournament. They are split into teams of 7. How many children are left over? **6**

A rowing boat can hold 6 people. There are 29 passengers waiting. How many boats will be needed to transport them all? **5**

Joseph has 33 sweets. He shares them equally between 5 friends then keeps the rest for himself. How many sweets do each of his friends get? **6**

A lift can hold a maximum of 8 people. 92 people are waiting to go in the lift. How many journeys will be needed for everyone to go up in the lift? **12**

There are 59 tickets left for an ice hockey match. The tickets are shared equally between 7 people and the rest are given to charity. How many tickets does each person get? **8**

43 people are going to a theme park. Each car can hold 5 people. How many cars are needed to take everyone to the theme park? **9**

Heather has 115 books to put away. Each box holds 11 books. She fills as many boxes as she can. How many books are left over? **5**

Division Tricks

For tricky divisions you can split the bigger number to make them easier to work out. Here's an example: ➡ $56 \div 4 = ?$

Split up the big number into two easier numbers. They should both be multiples of the smaller number.

56 ➡ 40 / 16

It's usually easiest if you make one of them a multiple of 10.

Divide these easier numbers by the smaller number...
$40 \div 4 = 10$
$16 \div 4 = 4$

... then add up the answers. $10 + 4 = 14$

Split up the big number to help you answer these questions.

78 ÷ 6	98 ÷ 7	69 ÷ 3
60 ÷ 6 = 10	**70** ÷ **7** = 10	**60** ÷ **3** = 20
18 ÷ 6 = 3	**28** ÷ **7** = 4	**9** ÷ **3** = 3
10 + 3 = 13	**10** + 4 = 14	**20** + 3 = 23

Fill in the boxes to complete these calculations.

42	÷	3	=	**14**	147	÷	7	=	**21**
64	÷	4	=	**16**	198	÷	9	=	**22**
114	÷	6	=	**19**	184	÷	8	=	**23**
96	÷	4	=	**24**	1608	÷	4	=	**402**
68	÷	2	=	**34**	2460	÷	6	=	**410**

If your child finds these questions tricky, get them to practise splitting large numbers into multiples of other numbers.

You can make dividing decimals easier by multiplying the decimal to make it a whole number.
Here's an example: ➡ $4.8 \div 4 = ?$

Multiply the decimal by 10 to make it a whole number. $4.8 \times 10 = 48$

Do the division using the whole number. $48 \div 4 = 12$

48 is 10 times bigger than 4.8, so the answer is 10 times too big. You need to divide by 10. $12 \div 10 = 1.2$

Fill in the boxes to complete the calculations.

3.2	÷	4	=	**0.8**	1.2	÷	4	=	**0.3**
4.5	÷	5	=	**0.9**	2.4	÷	3	=	**0.8**
7.7	÷	7	=	**1.1**	4.9	÷	7	=	**0.7**
3.6	÷	6	=	**0.6**	7.2	÷	8	=	**0.9**
6.3	÷	9	=	**0.7**	10.8	÷	9	=	**1.2**

Answer the questions below using division.

A pack of 4 scones costs £1.60. How much does each scone cost? £ **0.40**

Anna buys 1.6 kg of cheese. She shares it between 8 people. How much cheese does each person get? **0.2** kg

4 friends go swimming and it costs £8.40. How much does it cost for each person? £ **2.10**

A piece of string is 9.6 cm long. If you cut it into 8 equal pieces, how long will each piece be? **1.2** cm

Square & Cube Numbers

To square a number, multiply the number by itself: ➡ $3^2 = 3$ **squared** $= 3 \times 3 = 9$

To cube a number, multiply the number by itself twice: ➡ $2^3 = 2$ **cubed** $= 2 \times 2 \times 2 = 8$

Match each calculation with the correct answer.

4^2 36 121 4^3

1^3 64 5^3

11^2 125 1 9^2

6^2 16 27 81 3^3

Fill in the boxes to complete these calculations.

3^2	+	4	=	13	2^2	×	3	=	**12**
7^2	−	12	=	**37**	10^2	×	4	=	**400**
7	+	5^2	=	**32**	6^2	÷	2	=	**18**
9^2	+	9	=	**90**	5^2	×	2	=	**50**
12^2	−	14	=	**130**	4^2	÷	8	=	**2**

It's a good idea for your child to learn the first few square and cube numbers, so they don't have to work them out every time.

Fractions

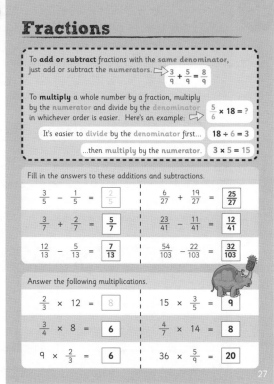

To **add or subtract** fractions with the **same denominator**, just add or subtract the **numerators**. ➡ $\frac{3}{9} + \frac{5}{9} = \frac{8}{9}$

To **multiply** a whole number by a fraction, multiply by the **numerator** and divide by the **denominator** in whichever order is easier. Here's an example: ➡ $\frac{5}{6} \times 18 = ?$

It's easier to **divide** by the **denominator** first... $18 \div 6 = 3$

...then **multiply** by the **numerator**. $3 \times 5 = 15$

Fill in the answers to these additions and subtractions.

$\frac{3}{5} - \frac{1}{5} = \frac{2}{5}$ $\frac{6}{27} + \frac{19}{27} = \frac{25}{27}$

$\frac{3}{7} + \frac{2}{7} = \frac{5}{7}$ $\frac{23}{41} - \frac{11}{41} = \frac{12}{41}$

$\frac{12}{13} - \frac{5}{13} = \frac{7}{13}$ $\frac{54}{103} - \frac{22}{103} = \frac{32}{103}$

Answer the following multiplications.

$\frac{2}{3} \times 12 = 8$ $15 \times \frac{3}{5} = 9$

$\frac{3}{4} \times 8 = 6$ $\frac{4}{7} \times 14 = 8$

$9 \times \frac{2}{3} = 6$ $36 \times \frac{5}{9} = 20$

If your child has difficulty doing fraction multiplications, get them to write down each step.

Mixed Calculations

BODMAS tells you which order operations should be done in a calculation. Operations are things like ÷, ×, + and −.

BODMAS = **B**rackets, **O**ther, **D**ivision, **M**ultiplication, **A**ddition, **S**ubtraction

Here's an example: ➡ $3 + 4 \times 5 = ?$ Other is things like squaring.

Do the Multiplication first as it is before Addition in BODMAS. $4 \times 5 = 20$

Then do the Addition. $20 + 3 = 23$

Use BODMAS to do these calculations. Circle the correct answer.

$15 \div 3 + 2 = $ ⑦ / 3 $8 + 32 \div 8 = $ 5 / ⑫ $27 - 6 \div 3 = $ ㉕ / 7

$12 \times 4 - 2 = $ 24 / ㊻ $7 + 3 \times 9 = $ 90 / ㉞ $9 + 3 \times 7 = $ ㉚ / 84

Fill in the boxes to complete the calculations.

$18 + 24 \div 3 = $	26	$90 - 8 \times 6 = $ **42**
$38 - 7 \times 4 = $	**10**	$56 \div 7 - 3 = $ **5**
$45 + 18 \div 9 = $	**47**	$60 - 5 \times 9 = $ **15**
$80 \div 8 + 12 = $	**22**	$17 + 8 \times 5 = $ **57**
$23 + 4 \times 9 = $	**59**	$38 - 30 \div 6 = $ **33**

Make sure your child knows what each letter in BODMAS stands for. Get them to practise writing out what each letter means.

When there are brackets in a calculation you need to work out whatever is inside them first. **B**rackets are first in **B**ODMAS.

BODMAS = **B**rackets, **O**ther, **D**ivision, **M**ultiplication, **A**ddition, **S**ubtraction

Here's an example: ➡ $(3 + 5) \times 7 = ?$

Do the calculation in brackets first. $3 + 5 = 8$

Then do the multiplication. $8 \times 7 = 56$

So the answer is: $(3 + 5) \times 7 = 56$

Put brackets into the calculations to make the answers correct.

$8 \times (6 + 2) = 64$ $(55 + 11) \div 11 = 6$

$(12 - 5) \times 5 = 35$ $10 \times (19 - 11) = 80$

$(10 - 4) \div 2 = 3$ $(16 + 32) \div 4 = 12$

$2 \times (4 + 3) = 14$ $42 \div (9 - 3) = 7$

Fill in the boxes to complete the calculations.

$(15 + 21) \div 3 = $	12	$(53 - 42) \times 6 = $ **66**
$63 \div (12 - 5) = $	**9**	$81 \div (16 - 7) = $ **9**
$(13 + 11) \div 6 = $	**4**	$(3 + 2) \times 8 = $ **40**
$(92 - 89) \times 4 = $	**12**	$(8 + 3) \times 11 = $ **121**
$(11 + 24) \div 7 = $	**5**	$48 \div (24 - 18) = $ **8**

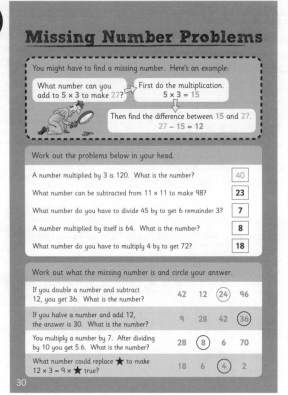

30 — Missing Number Problems

You might have to find a missing number. Here's an example:

> What number can you add to 5 × 3 to make 27?
> First do the multiplication. 5 × 3 = 15
> Then find the difference between 15 and 27. 27 − 15 = 12

Work out the problems below in your head.

A number multiplied by 3 is 120. What is the number? — 40

What number can be subtracted from 11 × 11 to make 98? — **23**

What number do you have to divide 45 by to get 6 remainder 3? — **7**

A number multiplied by itself is 64. What is the number? — **8**

What number do you have to multiply 4 by to get 72? — **18**

Work out what the missing number is and circle your answer.

If you double a number and subtract 12, you get 36. What is the number? — 42   12   (24)   96

If you halve a number and add 12, the answer is 30. What is the number? — 9   28   42   (36)

You multiply a number by 7. After dividing by 10 you get 5.6. What is the number? — 28   (8)   6   70

What number could replace ★ to make 12 × 3 = 9 × ★ true? — 18   6   (4)   2

30

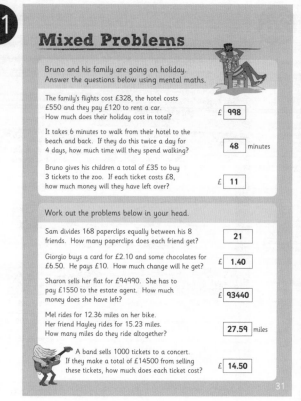

31 — Mixed Problems

Bruno and his family are going on holiday. Answer the questions below using mental maths.

The family's flights cost £328, the hotel costs £550 and they pay £120 to rent a car. How much does their holiday cost in total? — £ **998**

It takes 6 minutes to walk from their hotel to the beach and back. If they do this twice a day for 4 days, how much time will they spend walking? — **48** minutes

Bruno gives his children a total of £35 to buy 3 tickets to the zoo. If each ticket costs £8, how much money will they have left over? — £ **11**

Work out the problems below in your head.

Sam divides 168 paperclips equally between his 8 friends. How many paperclips does each friend get? — **21**

Giorgio buys a card for £2.10 and some chocolates for £6.50. He pays £10. How much change will he get? — £ **1.40**

Sharon sells her flat for £94990. She has to pay £1550 to the estate agent. How much money does she have left? — £ **93440**

Mel rides for 12.36 miles on her bike. Her friend Hayley rides for 15.23 miles. How many miles do they ride altogether? — **27.59** miles

A band sells 1000 tickets to a concert. If they make a total of £14500 from selling these tickets, how much does each ticket cost? — £ **14.50**

31

If your child has difficulty with any of these questions, get them to have another look at the methods earlier in the book.

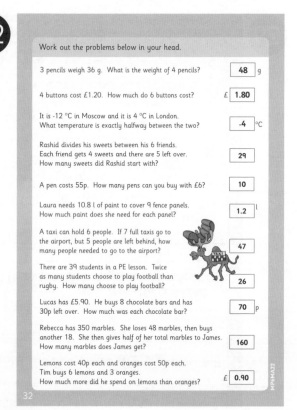

32

Work out the problems below in your head.

3 pencils weigh 36 g. What is the weight of 4 pencils? — **48** g

4 buttons cost £1.20. How much do 6 buttons cost? — £ **1.80**

It is -12 °C in Moscow and it is 4 °C in London. What temperature is exactly halfway between the two? — **-4** °C

Rashid divides his sweets between his 6 friends. Each friend gets 4 sweets and there are 5 left over. How many sweets did Rashid start with? — **29**

A pen costs 55p. How many pens can you buy with £6? — **10**

Laura needs 10.8 l of paint to cover 9 fence panels. How much paint does she need for each panel? — **1.2** l

A taxi can hold 6 people. If 7 full taxis go to the airport, but 5 people are left behind, how many people needed to go to the airport? — **47**

There are 39 students in a PE lesson. Twice as many students choose to play football than rugby. How many choose to play football? — **26**

Lucas has £5.90. He buys 8 chocolate bars and has 30p left over. How much was each chocolate bar? — **70** p

Rebecca has 350 marbles. She loses 48 marbles, then buys another 18. She then gives half of her total marbles to James. How many marbles does James get? — **160**

Lemons cost 40p each and oranges cost 50p each. Tim buys 6 lemons and 3 oranges. How much more did he spend on lemons than oranges? — £ **0.90**

32

MPNM4J2

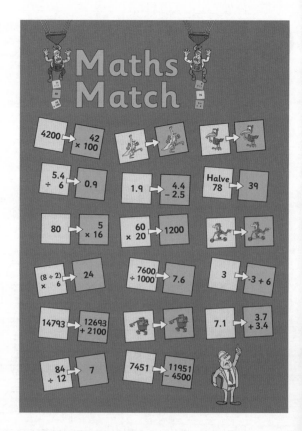

Maths Match

4200 → × 100

5.4 ÷ 6 → 0.9   1.9   4.4 − 2.5   Halve 78 → 39

80   5 × 16   60 × 20 → 1200

(8 ÷ 2) × 6 → 24   7600 ÷ 1000 → 7.6   3 → -3 + 6

14793   12693 + 2100   7.1   3.7 + 3.4

84 ÷ 12 → 7   7451   11951 − 4500

Division Facts

You can also use division facts to help you do tricky calculations. Here's an example: ➡️ **210 ÷ 3 = ?**

From your times tables you know that **21 ÷ 3 = 7**

210 is **10** times bigger than **21**. The answer must be **10** times bigger than **7**.   **7 × 10 = 70**

Draw an arrow between each calculation and its correct answer.

	4			2			6
240 ÷ 6 → 40			180 ÷ 9	20		300 ÷ 50	60

	3			5			900
120 ÷ 40	30		150 ÷ 30	50		81000 ÷ 9	9000

	8			4			7
720 ÷ 9	80		280 ÷ 70	40		4200 ÷ 60	70

Fill in the boxes to complete the calculations.

180	÷	6	=	30	100	÷	20	=
200	÷	4	=		3000	÷	50	=
810	÷	90	=		6300	÷	7	=
240	÷	30	=		4900	÷	70	=
540	÷	9	=		72000	÷	8	=

Multiplication

You can do some multiplications just by knowing your times tables. For harder multiplications you can split up one of the numbers. Here's an example: ⇨ **15 × 7 = ?**

Split the big number into **tens** and **units**.	**15** ⇨ **10 and 5**
Multiply the small number by the **tens**...	**7 × 10 = 70**
... then multiply it by the **units**.	**7 × 5 = 35**
Then add them together to get the answer.	**70 + 35 = 105**

Underline the calculation that equals the number in the circle.

150 ⇨	<u>25 × 6</u>	14 × 10	29 × 5	45 × 4
72 ⇨	3 × 40	13 × 4	12 × 6	14 × 8
39 ⇨	16 × 2	15 × 3	19 × 5	13 × 3
119 ⇨	20 × 6	14 × 8	17 × 7	16 × 9

Answer the questions below using multiplication.

Sam has 9 packets that each have 15 cabbage seeds inside.
How many seeds does she have altogether?

Eleanor has 6 pieces of ribbon that are each 21 cm long.
What is the total length of the ribbon pieces? 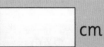 cm

A tin contains 19 biscuits. Solomon buys 8 tins.
How many biscuits has he bought?

Write the answers to the questions below.
See how fast you can do them all.

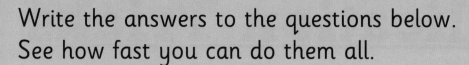

40	×	7	=	280	46	×	3	=
50	×	9	=		26	×	8	=
20	×	3	=		42	×	6	=
13	×	2	=		78	×	4	=
15	×	3	=		39	×	9	=
19	×	2	=		84	×	5	=
22	×	4	=		67	×	6	=
15	×	5	=		302	×	2	=
14	×	3	=		230	×	3	=
23	×	5	=		120	×	5	=
30	×	8	=		205	×	4	=
25	×	7	=		160	×	4	=
45	×	4	=		142	×	2	=
65	×	6	=		312	×	3	=
13	×	6	=		3004	×	2	=
19	×	7	=		4400	×	2	=
16	×	9	=		1020	×	3	=
32	×	8	=		2050	×	4	=

19

Multiplication Tricks

You can make multiplying decimal numbers easier by turning them into whole numbers. Here's an example: $\Rightarrow$ **0.6 × 4 = ?**

Multiply the decimal number by **10** to turn it into a whole number. **0.6 × 10 = 6**

Do the multiplication using the whole number. **6 × 4 = 24**

The answer is **10** times too big. Divide it by **10** to find the answer. **24 ÷ 10 = 2.4**

Fill in the boxes to complete the calculations.

0.4	×	4	=	1.6		0.5	×	3	=
0.6	×	5	=			0.9	×	8	=
0.3	×	9	=			0.8	×	6	=
0.2	×	8	=			0.7	×	7	=

Answer the questions below using multiplication.

A bar of chocolate costs £0.80.
How much do 8 bars of chocolate cost?   £

Eleanor needs 0.4 kg of flour to make 1 loaf of bread.
How much flour does she need to make 6 loaves?   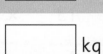 kg

12 people are having lunch. They each drink 0.6 l
of juice. How much juice do they drink altogether?   l

Jo carries 9 tins that each weigh 0.4 kg. Sam carries 11
tins that each weigh 0.3 kg. Who carries the heaviest load?

For tricky multiplications involving decimals, you can also use rounding to make them easier to work out. Here's an example: 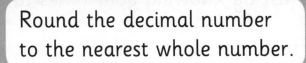 **6 × 1.99 = ?**

Round the decimal number to the nearest whole number.	**1.99** rounds up to **2.00** by adding **0.01**.
Work out the rounded multiplication.	**6 × 2.00 = 12.00**
Multiply what you rounded up by.	**6 × 0.01 = 0.06**
Then subtract the small number from the large one to find the answer.	**12.00 – 0.06 = 11.94**

Round the decimal number to the nearest whole number and fill in the boxes to complete these calculations.

2.99 × 3

3.00 × 3 = 9.00

0.01 × 3 = 0.03

9.00 – 0.03 = 8.97

1.80 × 5

☐ × ☐ = ☐

☐ × ☐ = ☐

☐ – ☐ = ☐

3.95 × 6

☐ × ☐ = ☐

☐ × ☐ = ☐

☐ – ☐ = ☐

Use the price list for Sue's Ices to answer the questions below.

How much does it cost to buy...

... 8 Choc Ices? £ ☐

... 4 Double Cones? £ ☐

... 5 Ice Lollies? £ ☐

Sue's Ices

Single Cone	£1.40
Double Cone	£1.99
Choc Ice	£0.95
Ice Lolly	£1.70

21

Division

You can do some divisions just by knowing your times tables:

42 ÷ 7 = ? ⟹ From your times tables you know that **7 × 6 = 42,** so the answer is **6.**

With some divisions you might be left with a remainder.
Here's an example: ⟹ **75 ÷ 8 = ?**

From your times tables you know that **8 × 9 = 72**.
The difference between 75 and 72 is **3**...
... so the answer is **9 remainder 3**.

Fill in the boxes below to give the answer and the remainder (r).

20 ÷ 6 =	3 r. 2	28 ÷ 8 =	☐ r. ☐
7 ÷ 3 =	☐ r. ☐	87 ÷ 9 =	☐ r. ☐
19 ÷ 5 =	☐ r. ☐	140 ÷ 12 =	☐ r. ☐
68 ÷ 7 =	☐ r. ☐	73 ÷ 11 =	☐ r. ☐
17 ÷ 4 =	☐ r. ☐	35 ÷ 9 =	☐ r. ☐
25 ÷ 3 =	☐ r. ☐	47 ÷ 11 =	☐ r. ☐
53 ÷ 7 =	☐ r. ☐	89 ÷ 12 =	☐ r. ☐
39 ÷ 6 =	☐ r. ☐	81 ÷ 7 =	☐ r. ☐

Answer the questions below using division.

Ed packs 38 eggs into boxes of 6. He eats the leftover eggs for his tea. How many eggs does he eat?

There are 58 people at a party. Each table seats 9 people. How many tables are filled up?

76 children want to play in a football tournament. They are split into teams of 7. How many children are left over?

A rowing boat can hold 6 people. There are 29 passengers waiting. How many boats will be needed to transport them all?

Joseph has 33 sweets. He shares them equally between 5 friends then keeps the rest for himself. How many sweets do each of his friends get?

A lift can hold a maximum of 8 people. 92 people are waiting to go in the lift. How many journeys will be needed for everyone to go up in the lift?

There are 59 tickets left for an ice hockey match. The tickets are shared equally between 7 people and the rest are given to charity. How many tickets does each person get?

43 people are going to a theme park. Each car can hold 5 people. How many cars are needed to take everyone to the theme park?

Heather has 115 books to put away. Each box holds 11 books. She fills as many boxes as she can. How many books are left over?

Division Tricks

For tricky divisions you can split the bigger number to make them easier to work out. Here's an example: ⟹ **56 ÷ 4 = ?**

Split up the big number into two easier numbers. They should both be multiples of the smaller number.

56 ⟶ **40**
⟶ **16**

It's usually easiest if you make one of them a multiple of 10.

Divide these easier numbers by the smaller number...

40 ÷ 4 = 10
16 ÷ 4 = 4

... then add up the answers.

10 + 4 = 14

Split up the big number to help you answer these questions.

78 ÷ 6			98 ÷ 7			69 ÷ 3		
60 ÷ 6 = 10			☐ ÷ ☐ = ☐			☐ ÷ ☐ = ☐		
18 ÷ 6 = 3			☐ ÷ ☐ = ☐			☐ ÷ ☐ = ☐		
10 + 3 = 13			☐ + ☐ = ☐			☐ + ☐ = ☐		

Fill in the boxes to complete these calculations.

42 ÷ 3 =	14		147 ÷ 7 =	☐
64 ÷ 4 =	☐		198 ÷ 9 =	☐
114 ÷ 6 =	☐		184 ÷ 8 =	☐
96 ÷ 4 =	☐		1608 ÷ 4 =	☐
68 ÷ 2 =	☐		2460 ÷ 6 =	☐

You can make dividing decimals easier by multiplying the decimal to make it a whole number.

Here's an example: 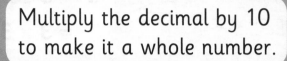 **4.8 ÷ 4 = ?**

Multiply the decimal by 10 to make it a whole number.   **4.8 × 10 = 48**

Do the division using the whole number.   **48 ÷ 4 = 12**

48 is 10 times bigger than **4.8**, so the answer is 10 times too big. You need to divide by 10.   **12 ÷ 10 = 1.2**

Fill in the boxes to complete the calculations.

3.2 ÷ 4 =	0.8	1.2 ÷ 4 =	
4.5 ÷ 5 =		2.4 ÷ 3 =	
7.7 ÷ 7 =		4.9 ÷ 7 =	
3.6 ÷ 6 =		7.2 ÷ 8 =	
6.3 ÷ 9 =		10.8 ÷ 9 =	

Answer the questions below using division.

A pack of 4 scones costs £1.60.
How much does each scone cost?   £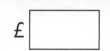

Anna buys 1.6 kg of cheese. She shares it between 8 people. How much cheese does each person get?   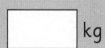 kg

4 friends go swimming and it costs £8.40.
How much does it cost for each person?   £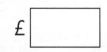

A piece of string is 9.6 cm long. If you cut it into 8 equal pieces, how long will each piece be?   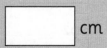 cm

Square & Cube Numbers

To square a number,
multiply the number by itself:

$3^2 = 3$ **squared**
$= 3 \times 3 = 9$

To cube a number,
multiply the number by itself twice:

$2^3 = 2$ **cubed**
$= 2 \times 2 \times 2 = 8$

Match each calculation with the correct answer.

4^2 36   121 4^3

1^3 64 5^3

125 1

11^2 9^2

27

6^2 16   81 3^3

Fill in the boxes to complete these calculations.

3^2	$+$	4	$=$	13	2^2	$\times$	3	$=$	
7^2	$-$	12	$=$		10^2	$\times$	4	$=$	
7	$+$	5^2	$=$		6^2	$\div$	2	$=$	
9^2	$+$	9	$=$		5^2	$\times$	2	$=$	
12^2	$-$	14	$=$		4^2	$\div$	8	$=$	

26

Fractions

To **add or subtract** fractions with the **same denominator**, just add or subtract the **numerators**. ⟹ $\dfrac{3}{9} + \dfrac{5}{9} = \dfrac{8}{9}$

To **multiply** a whole number by a fraction, multiply by the **numerator** and divide by the **denominator** in whichever order is easier. Here's an example: ⟹ $\dfrac{5}{6} \times 18 = ?$

| It's easier to **divide** by the **denominator** first... | $18 \div 6 = 3$ |

| ...then **multiply** by the **numerator**. | $3 \times 5 = 15$ |

Fill in the answers to these additions and subtractions.

$\dfrac{3}{5} - \dfrac{1}{5} = \boxed{\dfrac{2}{5}}$ $\qquad$ $\dfrac{6}{27} + \dfrac{19}{27} = \boxed{}$

$\dfrac{3}{7} + \dfrac{2}{7} = \boxed{}$ $\qquad$ $\dfrac{23}{41} - \dfrac{11}{41} = \boxed{}$

$\dfrac{12}{13} - \dfrac{5}{13} = \boxed{}$ $\qquad$ $\dfrac{54}{103} - \dfrac{22}{103} = \boxed{}$

Answer the following multiplications.

$\dfrac{2}{3} \times 12 = \boxed{8}$ $\qquad$ $15 \times \dfrac{3}{5} = \boxed{}$

$\dfrac{3}{4} \times 8 = \boxed{}$ $\qquad$ $\dfrac{4}{7} \times 14 = \boxed{}$

$9 \times \dfrac{2}{3} = \boxed{}$ $\qquad$ $36 \times \dfrac{5}{9} = \boxed{}$

Mixed Calculations

BODMAS tells you which order operations should be done in a calculation. Operations are things like ÷, ×, + and −.

BODMAS = **B**rackets, **O**ther, **D**ivision, **M**ultiplication, **A**ddition, **S**ubtraction

Here's an example: ⟹ **3 + 4 × 5 = ?**

Other is things like squaring.

Do the **M**ultiplication first as it is before **A**ddition in **BODMAS**.

4 × 5 = 20

Then do the **A**ddition. **20 + 3 = 23**

Use BODMAS to do these calculations. Circle the correct answer.

15 ÷ 3 + 2 = ⟨ (7) / 3

8 + 32 ÷ 8 = ⟨ 5 / 12

27 − 6 ÷ 3 = ⟨ 25 / 7

12 × 4 − 2 = ⟨ 24 / 46

7 + 3 × 9 = ⟨ 90 / 34

9 + 3 × 7 = ⟨ 30 / 84

Fill in the boxes to complete the calculations.

18 + 24 ÷ 3 = [26]   90 − 8 × 6 = [ ]

38 − 7 × 4 = [ ]   56 ÷ 7 − 3 = [ ]

45 + 18 ÷ 9 = [ ]   60 − 5 × 9 = [ ]

80 ÷ 8 + 12 = [ ]   17 + 8 × 5 = [ ]

23 + 4 × 9 = [ ]   38 − 30 ÷ 6 = [ ]

When there are brackets in a calculation you need to work out whatever is inside them first. **B**rackets are first in **B**ODMAS.

BODMAS = **B**rackets, **O**ther, **D**ivision, **M**ultiplication, **A**ddition, **S**ubtraction

Here's an example: $\Rightarrow$ **(3 + 5) × 7 = ?**

Do the calculation in brackets first.   **3 + 5 = 8**

Then do the multiplication.   **8 × 7 = 56**

So the answer is: **(3 + 5) × 7 = 56**

Put brackets into the calculations to make the answers correct.

8 × (6 + 2) = 64	55 + 11 ÷ 11 = 6
12 − 5 × 5 = 35	10 × 19 − 11 = 80
10 − 4 ÷ 2 = 3	16 + 32 ÷ 4 = 12
2 × 4 + 3 = 14	42 ÷ 9 − 3 = 7

Fill in the boxes to complete the calculations.

(15 + 21) ÷ 3 = 12	(53 − 42) × 6 =
63 ÷ (12 − 5) =	81 ÷ (16 − 7) =
(13 + 11) ÷ 6 =	(3 + 2) × 8 =
(92 − 89) × 4 =	(8 + 3) × 11 =
(11 + 24) ÷ 7 =	48 ÷ (24 − 18) =

Missing Number Problems

You might have to find a missing number. Here's an example:

What number can you add to **5 × 3** to make **27**? ➤ First do the multiplication.
5 × 3 = 15

Then find the difference between **15** and **27**.
27 − 15 = 12

Work out the problems below in your head.

A number multiplied by 3 is 120. What is the number? `40`

What number can be subtracted from 11 × 11 to make 98? `☐`

What number do you have to divide 45 by to get 6 remainder 3? `☐`

A number multiplied by itself is 64. What is the number? `☐`

What number do you have to multiply 4 by to get 72? `☐`

Work out what the missing number is and circle your answer.

If you double a number and subtract 12, you get 36. What is the number?	**42**	**12**	**(24)**	**96**
If you halve a number and add 12, the answer is 30. What is the number?	**9**	**28**	**42**	**36**
You multiply a number by 7. After dividing by 10 you get 5.6. What is the number?	**28**	**8**	**6**	**70**
What number could replace ★ to make 12 × 3 = 9 × ★ true?	**18**	**6**	**4**	**2**

Mixed Problems

Bruno and his family are going on holiday.
Answer the questions below using mental maths.

The family's flights cost £328, the hotel costs
£550 and they pay £120 to rent a car.
How much does their holiday cost in total?

£ ☐

It takes 6 minutes to walk from their hotel to the
beach and back. If they do this twice a day for
4 days, how much time will they spend walking?

☐ minutes

Bruno gives his children a total of £35 to buy
3 tickets to the zoo. If each ticket costs £8,
how much money will they have left over?

£ ☐

Work out the problems below in your head.

Sam divides 168 paperclips equally between his 8
friends. How many paperclips does each friend get?

☐

Giorgio buys a card for £2.10 and some chocolates for
£6.50. He pays £10. How much change will he get?

£ ☐

Sharon sells her flat for £94990. She has to
pay £1550 to the estate agent. How much
money does she have left?

£ ☐

Mel rides for 12.36 miles on her bike.
Her friend Hayley rides for 15.23 miles.
How many miles do they ride altogether?

☐ miles

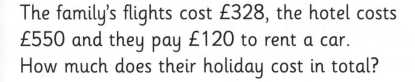

A band sells 1000 tickets to a concert.
If they make a total of £14500 from selling
these tickets, how much does each ticket cost?

£ ☐

Work out the problems below in your head.

3 pencils weigh 36 g. What is the weight of 4 pencils? ☐ g

4 buttons cost £1.20. How much do 6 buttons cost? £ ☐

It is -12 °C in Moscow and it is 4 °C in London.
What temperature is exactly halfway between the two? ☐ °C

Rashid divides his sweets between his 6 friends.
Each friend gets 4 sweets and there are 5 left over.
How many sweets did Rashid start with? ☐

A pen costs 55p. How many pens can you buy with £6? ☐

Laura needs 10.8 l of paint to cover 9 fence panels.
How much paint does she need for each panel? ☐ l

A taxi can hold 6 people. If 7 full taxis go to
the airport, but 5 people are left behind, how
many people needed to go to the airport? ☐

There are 39 students in a PE lesson. Twice
as many students choose to play football than
rugby. How many choose to play football? ☐

Lucas has £5.90. He buys 8 chocolate bars and has
30p left over. How much was each chocolate bar? ☐ p

Rebecca has 350 marbles. She loses 48 marbles, then buys
another 18. She then gives half of her total marbles to James.
How many marbles does James get? ☐

Lemons cost 40p each and oranges cost 50p each.
Tim buys 6 lemons and 3 oranges.
How much more did he spend on lemons than oranges? £ ☐